MY A TO Z BOOK

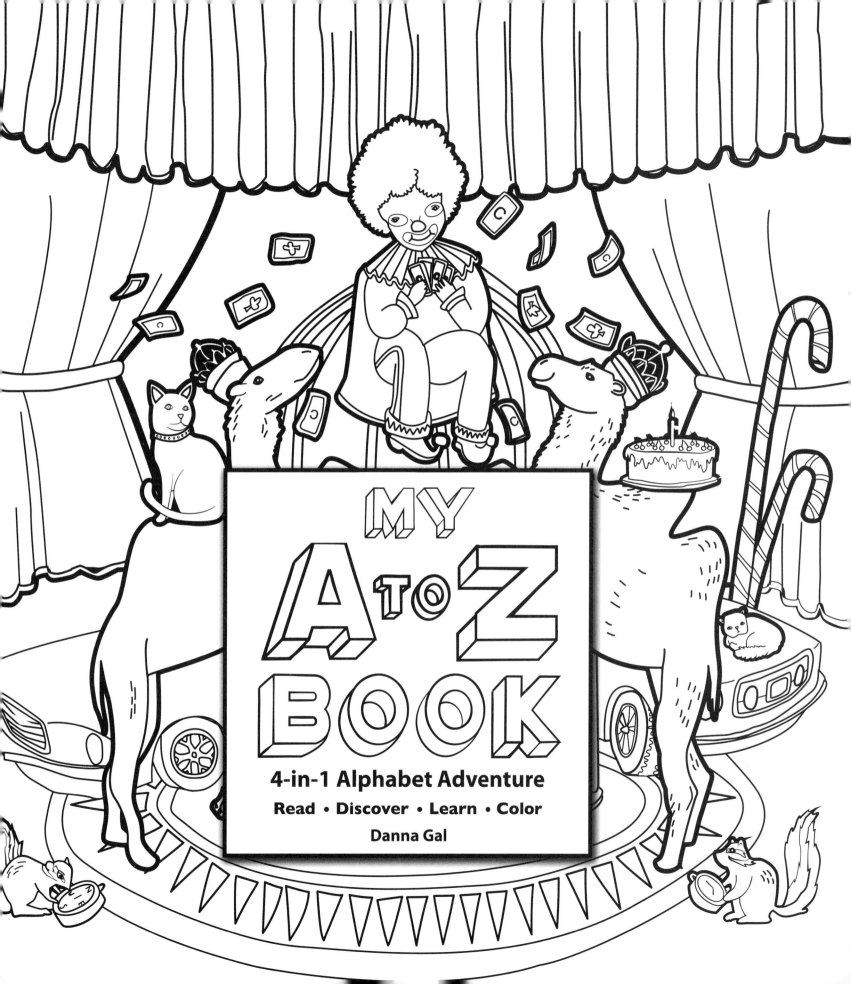

MY A TO Z BOOK

4-in-1 Alphabet Adventure

Read • Discover • Learn • Color

Danna Gal

First published by Chiltern Publishing in 2018
Chiltern Publishing
38 Copthorne Road
Croxley Green
Hertfordshire, WD3 4AQ, UK
www.MyAToZBook.com

Copyright © Danna Gal, 2018
Illustrations: Neta Manor
Graphic Design: Suela Kolpepaj

Acknowledgements
To my son, Adam David, for all the love and happiness you've given me

Special thanks to the Gal Family, the Wolt Family and Kate Afanasyeva

Printed in China

ISBN: 978-1-9999501-1-8

These places, letters and words are brought to life by:

_____

&

EPPEH

The Bunny Puppet

Can you find Eppeh, the hidden bunny, in each letter?

Welcome to

My A To Z Book was created to teach young children (ages 2–7) their ABCs while stimulating their imaginations, and to help them learn about the world around them.

It is an educational, interactive journey through the English Alphabet – a tactile learning experience for children, and a way to connect, engage and bond with their families. Adam and Eppeh go from A To Z while exploring universal settings and daily experiences familiar to any child. The Alphabet creates its own adventure in magical places which any child can relate to and teaches over 500 words in English.

There are four interactive ways to play and learn:

1. **Read the story about Adam and Eppeh's adventures**

2. **Color the elaborate illustrations**

3. **Spot Eppeh. Eppeh is a hidden bunny puppet in each letter. Can you find it?**

4. **Learn English vocabulary using the visual numbered method.**

My A To Z Book offers a wealth of games and ideas on how to enhance cognitive skills in children, and provides an interactive bonding experience for families: siblings and grandparents, parents and caregivers can all share the experience.

1. airport
2. axe
3. armor
4. acorn
5. armadillo
6. alien
7. aquarium
8. airplane
9. asteroid
10. archer
11. ant
12. arrows
13. apron
14. angel
15. astronaut
16. ambulance
17. antlers
18. antelope
19. acrobats
20. avocado
21. anteater
22. anchor
23. accordion
24. apple
25. arrivals

Adam and Eppeh are getting their passports.

All Airlines   Arrivals

Argentina
Australia
Austria
Antarctica
Algeria
Alabama

What for? To fly away from the airport.

1. beach
2. boat
3. bell
4. basketball
5. building
6. bridge
7. bird
8. bat
9. boy
10. ball
11. bucket
12. bee
13. baby
14. bed
15. bubbles
16. bathing suit
17. bananas
18. bug
19. bone
20. bear
21. bagel
22. bicycles
23. basket
24. bus
25. bodybuilder
26. butterfly
27. balloon
28. bottle
29. bag
30. blanket
31. broccoli
32. Batman
33. beard
34. book

Better be ready for fun at the beach.

Oh, a balloon! How high can it reach?

1. circus
2. curtain
3. chandelier
4. crowd
5. camera
6. cannon
7. cow
8. comb
9. cello
10. chair
11. chimp
12. cup
13. checkers
14. cap
15. cymbals
16. chipmunk
17. compass
18. caterpillar
19. crocodile
20. cage
21. cheetah
22. car
23. camel
24. cake
25. candy cane
26. crown
27. cat
28. cards
29. clown
30. candle

Adam and Eppeh catch a show.

Can you see a circus? Could you go?

Do you have a doctor? Eppeh comes along.

1. doctor's office
2. darts
3. discs
4. duck
5. doctor
6. duct tape
7. Darth Vader
8. drum
9. Dalmatian dog
10. door
11. dragon
12. daisy
13. daddy
14. daughter
15. dominos
16. doll
17. dolphin
18. dinosaur
19. Dalai Lama
20. donkey
21. drawer
22. dictionary
23. dollar

Do you see me play with dinosaurs while daddy sings a song?

1. Empire State Building
2. enclosure
3. eight
4. eggplant
5. earmuffs
6. envelope
7. elevator
8. elk
9. elephant
10. eagle
11. eye
12. emu
13. elf
14. escalator
15. eggs

What's the building that stands out the most?

The Empire State building! Where the American eagle takes post.

1. farm
2. flowers
3. freesia
4. fennel
5. fairy
6. foxglove
7. fuschia
8. football
9. five
10. fern
11. faucet
12. fox
13. fence
14. fire truck
15. Ferris wheel
16. fir
17. fire
18. flamingo
19. funnel
20. fish
21. freckles
22. fork
23. fly
24. fan
25. feet
26. frog
27. flute
28. falcon
29. feathers
30. Finland
31. Fiji
32. France
33. flags
34. farmhouse

It's fall at the farm. The flowers are bright.

The flags full of color. What a great sight.

Adam and Eppeh go golfing for fun.

1. golf course
2. grass
3. geese
4. gecko
5. gorilla
6. gazebo
7. ghost
8. globe
9. golf
10. gnome
11. goat
12. glove
13. goldfish
14. giraffe
15. gingerbread
16. gate
17. glasses
18. grandfather
19. guitar
20. grandmother
21. grapes
22. grandchild
23. grasshopper
24. golf ball
25. garlic

Go Adam! Go Eppeh! Get a hole in one!

1. house
2. hedgehog
3. heels
4. hairbrush
5. hat
6. hanger
7. handbag
8. herringbone
9. harp
10. hairdo
11. handle
12. helmet
13. hieroglyph
14. hula hoop
15. hamburger
16. hawk
17. hens
18. hammock
19. hamster
20. horseshoe
21. horse
22. hang glider
23. hot air balloon
24. headphones
25. hippopotamus
26. hoodie
27. handstand
28. hyena
29. hydra
30. horn
31. hills
32. helicopter
33. hair
34. hairdryer
35. hammer

Home, sweet home. What a happy house.

Here, there once was a hidden mouse.

1. island
2. iceberg
3. iguana
4. islander
5. iris
6. igloo
7. ice cream
8. ivy
9. ice skating rink
10. ice skaters
11. impala
12. iron
13. Indian princess

Ice cream and igloos? This island sure is busy.

Is the weather nice? If so, play all day!

Jump in the Jeep! Drive through the jumble.

1. jungle
2. juice
3. jellyfish
4. Jeep
5. jigsaw
6. jogger
7. jet
8. jackal
9. juggling
10. jar
11. jackrabbit
12. jaguar
13. jack-in-the-box
14. jasmine

Where to now? Into a jungle!

Keep your eyes open. What's about to happen?

1. kindergarten
2. kettle
3. kitchen
4. knot
5. kimono
6. knob
7. kaleidoscope
8. knee
9. kangaroo
10. knife
11. kiwi
12. king
13. kayak
14. koala
15. kids
16. karate
17. kiss
18. kiwi bird
19. kite
20. keys

Eppeh and Adam start kindergarten!

1. library
2. lemon tree
3. lotus
4. leaf
5. laptop
6. Legos
7. Lincoln
8. loudspeaker
9. llama
10. Lady Liberty
11. lockers
12. lock
13. love
14. lion
15. ladder
16. lizard
17. leprechaun
18. lantern
19. ladybug
20. lamb
21. lace
22. lollipop
23. lighthouse
24. lettuce
25. log
26. leak
27. leopard
28. letter
29. librarian
30. lemur
31. lamp

Look inside. Where do all these books belong?

In the library! Come along!

Many hidden treasures. Where to start?

1. museum
2. maze
3. moon
4. monk
5. mandolin
6. music
7. Matisse
8. Mona Lisa
9. mummy
10. mother
11. microscope
12. mushroom
13. magnet
14. mosquito
15. mobile
16. mermaid
17. match
18. Maltese cross
19. masks
20. microphone
21. moose
22. monkey
23. mammoth
24. mustache
25. man
26. medals
27. Mohawk
28. mouse
29. melon
30. moccasins
31. map
32. magnifying glass

Step inside the Museum of Art.

1. New York
2. nuts
3. NYPD
4. noodles
5. nun
6. net
7. nurse
8. newt
9. Nefertiti
10. Neanderthal
11. necklace
12. newsstand
13. newspaper
14. nails
15. Nessie
16. news
17. Nadal
18. Napoleon
19. Nazgûl
20. Nelson Mandela
21. needle
22. Nile
23. note
24. nail salon
25. nine

New York, New York.

The city that never sleeps.

Oh, office work can be so fun.

1. office
2. ostrich
3. orchid
4. owl
5. oysters
6. octopus
7. Oscar
8. office chair
9. oval
10. opossum
11. oranges
12. ocelot
13. omelet
14. olive oil
15. oar
16. otter
17. oboe

This is where Adam's dad gets his work done.

1. park
2. popcorn
3. panda
4. paws
5. plant
6. pizza
7. pond
8. parachute
9. parrot
10. playground
11. payphone
12. pigtails
13. pals
14. penguin
15. pigeon
16. postcard
17. pig
18. puzzle
19. present
20. pumpkin
21. porcupine
22. peacock
23. puppet
24. pineapple
25. pear
26. piano
27. parakeets
28. pipe
29. patch
30. pirate
31. palm

Central Park is not too far.

It's where the best playgrounds are.

1. quarry
2. quoll
3. queen
4. quill
5. question mark
6. quilt
7. quarters
8. quiver
9. quince
10. quail

A queen with a quill is quite a scene.

Do you think this queen is nice or mean?

1. restaurant
2. reindeer
3. refrigerator
4. rhinoceros
5. rollercoaster
6. rain
7. radio
8. robot
9. rummy
10. Robin Hood
11. rug
12. rat
13. rollerblades
14. rabbit
15. raisin
16. raspberry juice
17. Rocky Mountains
18. rainbow
19. raven
20. railway
21. rocket
22. radish
23. rose
24. raccoon

Rainy or not, Adam wants to go eat.

A restaurant around the corner serves the best treats.

This stadium is busy! What things do you see?

Adam and Eppeh are filled with glee!

1. stadium
2. Santa
3. socks
4. sneakers
5. spectators
6. shark
7. sun
8. stork
9. star
10. skyscraper
11. skateboard
12. sunflower
13. seashells
14. spade
15. saxophone
16. seal
17. sandwich
18. spoon
19. strawberry
20. seven
21. soccer
22. snail
23. samurai
24. sheep
25. scorpion
26. scarf
27. snake
28. spider
29. scissors
30. Sphinx
31. statue
32. swan
33. spaceship
34. skier
35. sunglasses

The toy store is one of our favorite places.

1. toy store
2. tricycle
3. tambourine
4. trumpet
5. trombone
6. teddy bear
7. tennis ball
8. train
9. thimble
10. troll
11. teepee
12. tiger
13. tractor
14. telescope
15. truck
16. twins
17. tree
18. teeth
19. toothbrush
20. television
21. tulip
22. turtle
23. table
24. typewriter
25. tank
26. toy soldier
27. telephone
28. triangle
29. tank top
30. turkey
31. tennis racket
32. toad
33. toes

Can't you tell? Look at our faces!

1. university
2. Uncle Sam
3. UFO
4. uakari
5. unicorn
6. umbrella
7. unicycle
8. underwear
9. uniform

Red, white and blue, United We Stand.

On July 4th we celebrate our Independence with Uncle Sam.

Volcanoes are big. Be careful! It's hot!

Lava pours through the valley. Touch we must not!

1. wrestling ring
2. watch
3. whale
4. wrestler
5. windmill
6. whistle
7. window
8. willow
9. wasp
10. wine
11. witch
12. wizard
13. watermelon
14. wheelbarrow
15. watermill
16. wagon
17. wolf
18. wheel
19. wheat
20. wild boar
21. wrench
22. wand
23. wig
24. windmill
25. wishbone

Worldwide wrestlers fight for title and prize.

Witches and wizards watch with eyes open wide.

1. xylophone store
2. xylophone
3. X-Files
4. x-ray

Xylophone here. Xylophone there. Xylophones are everywhere.

One big. One small. We should try to play them all.

A huge yacht. Yippee, it's filled with such fun.

1. yard
2. yoga
3. yak
4. Yankees hat
5. yogurt
6. Yoda
7. yin yang
8. yo-yo
9. yarn
10. yacht

Put your Yankees hat on to block out the sun!

Adam and Eppeh had such an adventure!

1. zoo
2. zero
3. Zulu
4. zipper
5. zebra
6. Zeppelin
7. Zamboni
8. Zorro
9. zucchini

The zoo ends our vacation! An amazing destination!

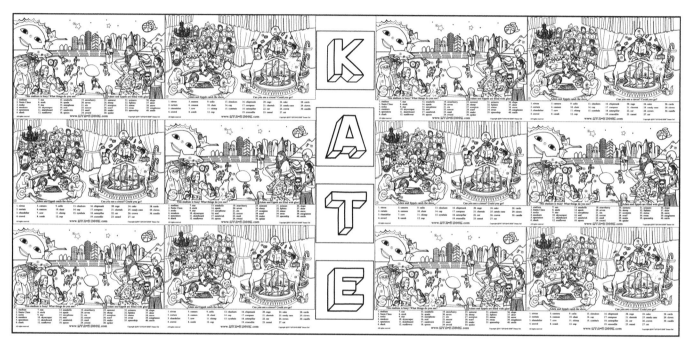

My A To Z Rug is an International Design Award Winning Product
For more info please watch our trailer :
www.myatozbook.com

MY A TO Z TILE™
LOVE

Color your life with My A To Z Children's educational products.
Use at home, in class, at playdates & birthday parties.
Build hundreds of words, names, initials, blessings, quotes, all created by you.
My A To Z Tile connects literacy and art.
Super easy and fun!

MY A TO Z TILE +™
ADAM

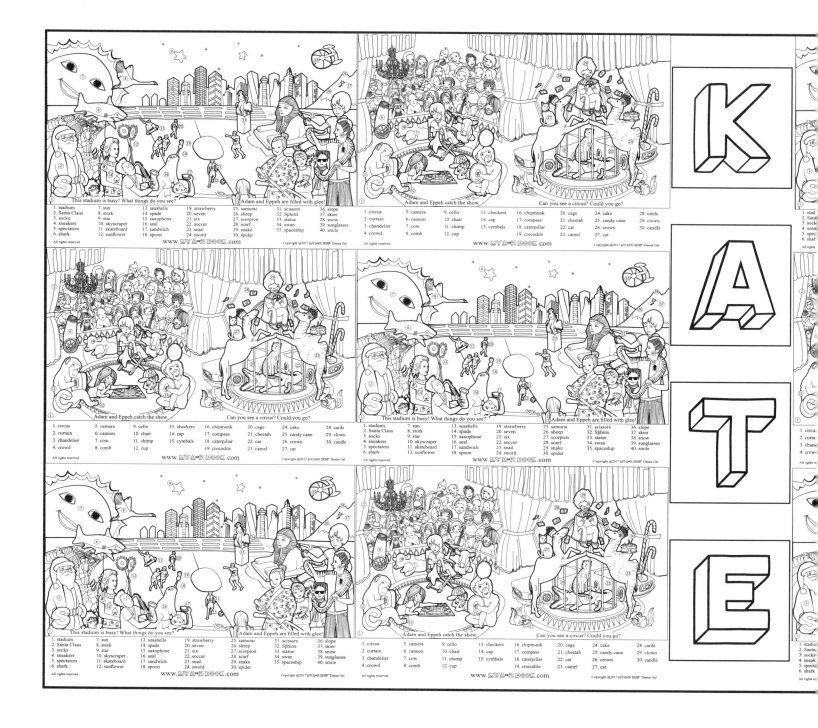

About the author

Gal's love of language, art, culture and design began when she was a young girl growing up in Israel. About her first picture book, Danna says, "I was inspired to create this story after giving birth to my son, Adam, to encourage him to become bilingual. Reading him *My A To Z Book* allowed me to connect and appreciate the beautiful world around us, expanding our horizons and bonding together as a loving family. No matter where we live, we can enjoy the English language and learn any language we wish. You can never give too much love and nurturing to a child. With this book you will find an amazing experience to connect and enrich your child's life."

Danna now lives and works in New York City.
Her website is
www.myatozbook.com.